# PLAY-ALONG SOUL
## WITH A LIVE BAND!

# FREE bonus material

Download band scores and parts to your computer.

# Visit www.hybridpublications.com

Registration is free and easy.


Your registration code is: AS546

# PLAY-ALONG SOUL
## WITH A LIVE BAND!

**WISE PUBLICATIONS**
part of The Music Sales Group
London / New York / Paris / Sydney / Copenhagen / Berlin / Madrid / Tokyo

Published by
**WISE PUBLICATIONS**
14-15 Berners Street, London W1T 3LJ, UK.

Exclusive Distributors:
**MUSIC SALES LIMITED**
Distribution Centre, Newmarket Road, Bury St Edmunds, Suffolk IP33 3YB, UK.
**MUSIC SALES PTY LIMITED**
20 Resolution Drive, Caringbah, NSW 2229, Australia.

Order No. AM991903
ISBN 978-1-84772-288-1
This book © Copyright 2008 Wise Publications, a division of Music Sales Limited.

Compiled by Nick Crispin
Edited by Fiona Bolton
Music arranged by Paul Honey
Music processed by Paul Ewers Music Design
Song Background Notes by Michael Heatley
Cover design by Adela Casacuberta
Cover photograph courtesy Gareth Brown / Corbis
Text photographs courtesy LFI
Printed in the EU

CD recorded, mixed and mastered by Jonas Persson
Flute: John Whelan
Keyboard: Paul Honey
Guitar: Arthur Dick
Bass: Don Richardson
Drums: Chris Baron

**YOUR GUARANTEE OF QUALITY**
As publishers, we strive to produce every book to the highest commercial standards.
This book has been carefully designed to minimise awkward page turns and to make playing
from it a real pleasure.
Particular care has been given to specifying acid-free, neutral-sized paper made from
pulps which have not been elemental chlorine bleached. This pulp is from farmed
sustainable forests and was produced with special regard for the environment.
Throughout, the printing and binding have been planned to ensure a sturdy, attractive
publication which should give years of enjoyment.
If your copy fails to meet our high standards, please inform us and we will gladly replace it.

www.musicsales.com

# Song Background Notes

## Cry To Me
*Solomon Burke*

The gospel fervour of this offering from Philadelphia-born Solomon Burke caught the ear of many on its release, and was perhaps not surprising bearing in mind he started out as a preacher before turning to secular soul. The Pretty Things and The Rolling Stones have both made cover versions of the song, but it was in 1987, when used in the film *Dirty Dancing*, in the famous scene in which Baby and Johnny seduce each other whilst dancing, that another generation awoke to the song's power. Mary J. Blige inducted Burke into the Rock And Roll Hall of Fame in 2001.

## I Get The Sweetest Feeling
*Jackie Wilson*

Three times a hit in Britain, this feel-good track from soul legend Jackie Wilson was a US hit in the late 1960s. It started life as a Motown song co-written by Van McCoy (of 'The Hustle' fame) and Alicia Evelyn, but quickly became Wilson's own with help from orchestrator Willie Henderson. After the chart-topping success of the Claymation video-led re-release of 'Reet Petite' in 1986, two years after Wilson's death, this track was also re-released and peaked at No.3 in the UK Chart. The song was used in the movie *High Fidelity*, and cover versions have been recorded by Will Young and Atomic Kitten Liz McClarnon.

## I Got You (I Feel Good)
*James Brown*

Good things come to those who wait. Godfather of soul James Brown originally wrote this song in 1962 for one of his backing singers, Yvonne Fair, but liked it so much he kept it for himself. He took it into the studio in 1964, but a record label dispute held up release. Undaunted, he recorded it again in 1965 and it became the first of many gold records to emerge from Criteria Studios in Miami where *Saturday Night Fever* would later be created. James Brown's signature song, it contains many of his musical trademarks including horn riffs, tempo changes and hollers.

## In The Midnight Hour
*Wilson Pickett*

After an initial hitless year as a recording artist, time was running out for Wilson Pickett, but he stopped the clock in 1965 with this track. Producer Jerry Wexler sent the singer to the hot music city of Memphis, where he wrote this song (and later many other hits) with guitarist Steve Cropper of Booker T & the MG's. The rhythm was designed to suit a then-current dance craze, 'the jerk'. Roxy Music would give the song an unlikely glam-pop makeover when they re-formed in the late 1970s, reflecting ex-soulboy Bryan Ferry's youthful listening habits.

## Knock On Wood
*Eddie Floyd*

The similarity between Eddie Floyd's biggest hit 'Knock On Wood' and Wilson Pickett's 'In The Midnight Hour' may have stemmed from co-writer Steve Cropper, who assisted both singers, and stopped the former being released until 1966, the year after 'In The Midnight Hour' made it into the charts. 'Knock On Wood' was written on a stormy night, hence the lyrical reference to thunder and lightning, and may well have been intended for Otis Redding, whose belated duet version of the song with Carla Thomas emerged in 1967. The song was also covered successfully by disco diva Amii Stewart (UK No.6, 1979) and David Bowie (UK No.10, 1974).

## Son Of A Preacher Man
*Dusty Springfield*

The success of the album *Dusty In Memphis*, of which this was the killer cut, underlined the fact that soul comes from within and is not determined by skin colour. The former Mary O'Brien had travelled to the Stax studios in 1968 and was offered the song only after Aretha Franklin turned it down. By the time Lady Soul reconsidered, Dusty's version had become definitive. A transatlantic Top 10 entry in early 1969, this would be Dusty Springfield's last hit for 20 years. The song has been covered by innumerable female singers but it was the original that featured in the 1994 film *Pulp Fiction*.

## Soul Man
*Sam & Dave*

Among the intros of Stax Records' many memorable hits, the guitar lick that introduces 'Soul Man', played by ace guitarist Steve Cropper, is the most recognisable. The song proved to be the career peak of Sam (Moore) and Dave (Prater), who, after its No.2 US pop success in 1967, found their relationship and career on the skids. The song itself however, written by Isaac Hayes and David Porter and based on the famous 'Bo Diddley' rhythm, was revived for the big screen over a decade later by the Blues Brothers. Its lyrics also made it an anthem for the black consciousness and black pride movements, the concept of soul linked with self-worth and community.

## Stand By Me
*Ben E. King*

This song was only Ben E. King's second solo release after leaving the Drifters in 1960. Twenty-seven years later it topped the UK chart and revived his by-then waning career. It was boosted by use as the title song of a Stephen King horror movie, but the inspiration of the song had been the gospel group once fronted by Sam Cooke. 'I took it from a spiritual the Soul Stirrers did,' said King, co-writer with producers Jerry Leiber and Mike Stoller. Someone else who had listened to the original release was John Lennon, who covered it on his 1975 collection of classic oldies, *Rock And Roll,* turning it into a hit of his own.

## Tired Of Being Alone
*Al Green*

Al Green, or the Reverend Al Green as he now is, brought a gospel purity to the soul world, assisted by Memphis producer Willie Dixon who would go on to be employed by Wet Wet Wet and others in later years. They may have sought his magic, but it was Green alone who had the voice. Written in late 1968, it proved problematical to record and as such took until 1971 to become his first US Top 40 hit. A signature track since appearing on *Al Green Gets Next To You*, the song featured in the movie *Dead Presidents*, in which Green is seen singing on a TV set.

# Try A Little Tenderness
## *Otis Redding*

Written by Irving King (a pseudonym used by the song-writing duo James Campbell and Reginald Connelly) and Harry M. Woods, this song dates back to 1933 and crooner Bing Crosby. Aretha Franklin was the first to record it soul-style in 1962, but all subsequent performances by the likes of Rod Stewart and Tina Turner have referenced Otis Redding's definitive 1966 version which progresses from balladic beginning to stomping climax in three and a half minutes. The only version Otis knew, by idol and mentor, Sam Cooke, featured just two verses as it was part of a live medley, so he performed it that way too. The song was brought to a new generation on the big screen in 1991 by *The Commitments*.

Ben E. King

James Brown

Dusty Springfield

Otis Redding

Sam & Dave

Wilson Pickett

# Cry To Me

Words & Music by Bert Russell

Demo track: Track 02
Backing track: Track 12

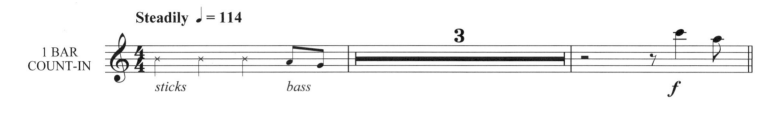

# I Get The Sweetest Feeling

Words & Music by Van McCoy & Alicia Evelyn

Demo track: Track 03
Backing track: Track 13

# I Got You (I Feel Good)

Words & Music by James Brown

Demo track: Track 04
Backing track: Track 14

**Moderate rock feel** ♩ = 140

14

rall.

# In The Midnight Hour

Words & Music by Steve Cropper & Wilson Pickett

Demo track: Track 05
Backing track: Track 15

**Steady rock feel** ♩ = 108

rall.

# Knock On Wood

### Words & Music by Steve Cropper & Eddie Floyd

Demo track: Track 06
Backing track: Track 16

**Moderate funk** ♩ = 104

# Son Of A Preacher Man

Words & Music by John Hurley & Ronnie Wilkins

Demo track: Track 07
Backing track: Track 17

# Soul Man

## Words & Music by Isaac Hayes & David Porter

Demo track: Track 08
Backing track: Track 18

# Stand By Me

### Words & Music by Ben E. King, Jerry Leiber & Mike Stoller

Demo track: Track 09
Backing track: Track 19

# Tired Of Being Alone

Words & Music by Al Green

Demo track: Track 10
Backing track: Track 20

**Moderately** ♩ = 98

# Try A Little Tenderness

### Words & Music by Harry Woods, Jimmy Campbell & Reg Connelly

Demo track: Track 11
Backing track: Track 21

rall.

123456789

# Also available...

# PLAY-ALONG WITH A JAZZ *Jazz* TRIO

Birdland *Weather Report*
Cantaloupe Island *Herbie Hancock*
Desafinado (Slightly Out Of Tune) *Antonio Carlos Jobim*
Fly Me To The Moon (In Other Words) *Julie London*
Let's Get Lost *Chet Baker*
So What *Miles Davis*
Straight No Chaser *Thelonious Monk*
Take Five *Dave Brubeck*
Take The 'A' Train *Duke Ellington*
When The Saints Go Marching In *Louis Armstrong*

Each edition contains music in melody line arrangements, a CD with professional 'soundalike' performances and backing tracks, plus free internet downloads.

Each edition contains music in melody line arrangements, a CD with professional 'soundalike' performances and backing tracks, plus free internet downloads.

# PLAY-ALONG BLUES WITH A LIVE BAND!

Baby What You Want Me To Do? *Jimmy Reed*
Call It Stormy Monday (But Tuesday Is Just As Bad) *T-Bone Walker*
Hi-Heel Sneakers *Tommy Tucker*
I'd Rather Go Blind *Etta James*
The Lady Sings The Blues *Billie Holiday*
Need Your Love So Bad *Fleetwood Mac*
Please Send Me Someone To Love *Percy Mayfield*
Sweet Home Chicago *Robert Johnson*
The Thrill Is Gone *B. B. King*
Wang Dang Doodle *Koko Taylor*

BLUES ORDER NUMBERS...
Alto Saxophone *AM991969*
Clarinet *AM991958*
Flute *AM991947*
Trombone *AM992882*
Trumpet *AM991980*

ALL TITLES ARE AVAILABLE FROM YOUR LOCAL MUSIC RETAILER.
IN CASE OF DIFFICULTY, CONTACT THE MARKETING DEPARTMENT,
MUSIC SALES LIMITED, NEWMARKET ROAD, BURY ST EDMUNDS, SUFFOLK IP33 3YB, UK

marketing@musicsales.co.uk

# CD Track Listing

1 Tuning Note

DEMONSTRATION TRACKS
2 Cry To Me (Russell) The International Music Network Limited.

3 I Get The Sweetest Feeling (McCoy/Evelyn) T M Music Limited.

4 I Got You (I Feel Good) (Brown) Lark Music Limited.

5 In The Midnight Hour (Cropper/Pickett) Carlin Music Corporation.

6 Knock On Wood (Cropper/Floyd) Universal Music Publishing Limited/Warner/Chappell Music Limited.

7 Son Of A Preacher Man (Hurley/Wilkins) Sony/ATV Music Publishing (UK) Limited.

8 Soul Man (Hayes/Porter) Rondor Music (London) Limited. Warner/Chappell Music Limited.

9 Stand By Me (King/Lieber/Stoller) Hornall Brothers Music Limited.

10 Tired Of Being Alone (Green) Burlington Music Company Limited/Universal Music Publishing Limited.

11 Try A Little Tenderness (Woods/Campbell/Connelly) Campbell Connelly & Company Limited.


BACKING TRACKS
12 Cry To Me

13 I Get The Sweetest Feeling

14 I Got You (I Feel Good)

15 In The Midnight Hour

16 Knock On Wood

17 Son Of A Preacher Man

18 Soul Man

19 Stand By Me

20 Tired Of Being Alone

21 Try A Little Tenderness

To remove your CD from the plastic sleeve,
Lift the small lip to break the perforations.
Replace the disc after use for convenient storage.